Stephenson Power

The Story of George and Robert Stephenson

Rocket

Ken Smith

• Tyneside Trailblazers •

Tyne Bridge Publishing

Acknowledgments:

The author would like to thank the following:
Andy Guy, researcher and writer, for his kind help and advice in the preparation of this book and for permission to use illustrations from his collection; the staff of Newcastle City Library; Barbara Harris of the Newcastle Mining Institute for her help in consulting the Institute's library.

The publishers gratefully acknowledge the assistance of the Heritage Lottery Fund in the production of this book, the invaluable support of Ian Ayris, and the Robert Stephenson Trust.

Illustrations acknowledgments: unless otherwise indicated illustrations are reproduced from the collections of Newcastle Libraries & Information Service.

Printed by Elanders Hindson, North Tyneside

Front cover:
Detail from *The High Level Bridge*, 1849, by J.W. Carmichael ©University of Newcastle upon Tyne.

Cover design: Anthony Flowers

If you have enjoyed this book you may also enjoy *Steam and Speed: Railways of Tyne and Wear from the Earliest Days* by Andy Guy, Tyne Bridge Publishing, 2003

ISBN: 1857951867

Published by City of Newcastle upon Tyne
Education & Libraries Directorate
Newcastle Libraries & Information Service,
Tyne Bridge Publishing, 2003

www.tynebridgepublishing.co.uk

Contents

A Cottage by the Tyne 5

The Sundial 9

Locomotive Fever 12

The Geordie Lamp 17

A Quaker Railway 22

Rocket to Success 26

The Bridge Builder 31

Father and Son 36

Chronology 39

Some sources 40

The locomotive Billy *on show on the upper deck at the Newcastle end of Robert Stephenson's High Level Bridge c.1885.* Billy, *not to be confused with William Hedley's* Puffing Billy, *is now on display at the Stephenson Railway Museum, North Tyneside. The engine is generally believed to have been built by Robert Stephenson & Co. in 1826. However, it may be a George Stephenson Killingworth engine of earlier date.*

Billy *worked on the Springwell Colliery Railway until 1868 and was then transferred to the Killingworth line, retiring in 1879. It took part in the 1881 George Stephenson Centenary celebrations before being displayed on the High Level Bridge.*

Left: the memorial to steam locomotive and railway pioneer George Stephenson at the junction of Neville Street and Westgate Road, Newcastle. It was erected in 1862. (Photographed in 1965.)

Right: the High Level Bridge. It was designed by Robert Stephenson and opened by Queen Victoria in 1849. Spanning the Tyne, the bridge brought the railway from the south into Newcastle for the first time and could be regarded as Robert Stephenson's best memorial. (Photographed in 2002.)

A Cottage by the Tyne

A statue of a man stands at the junction of Westgate Road and Neville Street in Newcastle city centre. People and cars hurry by with scarcely a glance at this monument to George Stephenson, the pioneering locomotive engineer who ushered in the era of steam railways.

Nearby, is the city's elegantly impressive Central Station and only a short distance further away is the magnificent High Level Bridge across the River Tyne. This bridge is the work of Stephenson's son, Robert. The huge iron structure, supported by massive sandstone pillars, was built to bring the railway from London into Newcastle for the first time.

A short distance beyond the Victorian grandeur of the Central Station, on banks high above the river, lies the site of Newcastle's Forth Street locomotive works, where the famous engine *Rocket* was built.

George Stephenson came from a poor, underprivileged background, yet through his spirited efforts, his passion for the locomotive and technical genius, he rose to become one of the world's most famed engineers.

George did not invent the locomotive but he played a major role in perfecting it and making it into a workable iron horse of incalculable benefit to mankind. He also demon-

Andy Guy

strated conclusively that steam railways were an efficient form of transport and pioneered the early techniques of steam railway building.

His son, Robert, also played a key role in developing the locomotive and railways. He became managing partner of the Forth Street Works at the age of 20 and later masterminded the building of *Rocket*. In addition, Robert achieved renown in the field of civil engineering, leaving to posterity a series of remarkable bridges.

George was the son of an ordinary working man, his father being totally dependent on selling his labour to provide for his family and children. George was born on June 9 1781 in a humble cottage on the banks of the River Tyne at Wylam, a village to the west of Newcastle. He was one of six children. The family's poverty meant that his parents and five of the children, including George, all had to live together in one room of the house. The remaining rooms were occupied by three other families.

Andy Guy

The cottage at Wylam where George Stephenson was born in 1781. The family lived in just one room of the house. Other mining families occupied the remaining rooms.

His father, Robert, like countless other men in the North-East, found employment in coal mining, for centuries the life-blood of the region. Robert was a fireman, stoking the pumping engine at Wylam Colliery. The engine was used to pump water from the mine to prevent flooding.

A waggonway of wooden rails to transport the coal ran past the cottage from Wylam Colliery to staiths (coal-loading jetties) at Lemington on the outskirts of Newcastle. From there, the coal was carried in keels (small boats) down the Tyne to sailing ships waiting in the lower reaches of the river, beyond Newcastle's 18th Century bridge of low arches.

The waggons were drawn along the rails by horses. This method of taking coal to the river from the pits was a familiar sight on Tyneside in the 18th and early 19th centuries. Waggonways and staiths were essential to the area's economy.

But the boy destined to play such a leading role in the

world did not stay long at Wylam. At the age of eight George said farewell to the stone cottage. Robert had obtained a job as a fireman at Dewley Burn Pit, Throckley, a few miles to the east. The family moved with him. They stayed there for six years.

However, the Dewley Burn Pit then shut down and Robert was forced to look for alternative work. A new pit, known as the Duke's Winning after its owner, the Duke of Northumberland, opened at Jolly's Close in the Newburn area. Robert found a job there. But this mine did not last long and he had to look for yet another job. He found one at the Water Row Pit, near Newburn.

George had various jobs as a boy. One of the earliest was as a "picker" at the Dewley Burn Pit. This involved extracting debris such as stones from the coal. When he reached the age of 10 he became a horse driver at a pit in Black Callerton.

However, at 14 he began following in his father's footsteps and became an assistant fireman at Dewley Burn under

The house at Willington Quay where Robert Stephenson was born in 1803. The Ballast Hill can be seen just behind.

his father. Then, following the closure of this mine, he became a fully-fledged fireman, working at two other pits in the area. Afterwards, he joined his father at the Water Row Pit.

It was at Water Row in particular that the son's mechanical talents came to the fore. George began to gain a reputation for his ability to mend machinery. He was so successful

George Stephenson 1781–1848
WATER ROW, NEWBURN
From 1798 to 1801 George Stephenson was in charge of Robert Hawthorn's new pumping engine at Water Row Pit, where George's father, Robert was fireman.
Tyne and Wear County Council

Andy Guy

that at the age of 17 he was put in control of the Water Row pumping engine.

In 1801, he obtained a job as brakesman at Black Callerton Colliery's Dolly Pit, in control of the winding engine which brought coal to the surface and lowered and raised men in and out of the mine.

But this son of a pit surface worker clearly wanted to develop his talents and he saw education as a means of progressing as a skilled man. George had remained uneducated throughout his boyhood. The family simply did not have the money to send their children to school. However, at the age of 18 he began going to night classes with an unofficial teacher in Walbottle village and within a few years had achieved basic literacy skills.

Soon, however, George's life was to take a new turn when he fell in love with a woman 12 years older than him. She was Frances Henderson, known as Fanny, who worked as a servant at a farm in the Black Callerton area where George had lodgings.

George and Fanny were married at Newburn Church in November 1802. The newly-weds moved to Willington Quay, near Wallsend, on the banks of the Tyne east of Newcastle. It was familiar accommodation to George – they lived in one room. It was all a Tyneside pit worker could expect in those days of extremely hard work and tough conditions. The rest of the cottage housed other families.

Sailing ships, returning from their coal voyages to London and other ports would unload their ballast at various points along the Tyne. Hills of ballast would thus be formed as more and more material was added. One of these hills was at Willington Quay and George's job was as brakesman in charge of the stationary engine which pulled full waggons to the top of this mound by means of cables.

Part of Willington Quay in 1831.

But operating the engine was not his only source of income. To earn extra money he put his practical abilities to work by making and mending shoes and boots in his spare time. He also repaired clocks.

George and Fanny's only son, Robert, was born in the cottage at Willington Quay on October 16 1803. Robert, like his father, was destined to become one of the great names in engineering history.

The Sundial

The family did not stay long at Willington Quay. The year 1804 saw George, Fanny and their baby son move to Killingworth Colliery, a few miles to the north of Newcastle. The young father had been appointed a brakesman at the colliery and the family lived in a house at West Moor, later to become known as Dial Cottage.

It was in this home that the couple's daughter, named after her mother, was born in 1805. However, the baby only lived for three weeks. Worse was to come. Tragedy struck again when Fanny, who had been in poor health, died of consumption at the age of 37 in the following year.

It may be that George could not bear to stay at West Moor after the traumatic loss of his wife and daughter. Perhaps he needed a period away from Tyneside to take stock of his situation. Whatever the reason, George went off to work for a short time in Scotland, leaving his small son in the care of a local woman. He probably walked all the way.

The promising young mechanic suffered a new blow several months later when he returned to Northumberland to find that his father Robert had been blinded. A blast of steam had been accidentally released from an engine into his face. The son resolved to support his father and mother for the rest of their lives. Such serious accidents involving working men, often fatal, were common in mining areas.

Andy Guy

Dial Cottage, West Moor, near Killingworth, to which George, his wife, Fanny, and their baby son Robert moved in 1804. The sundial can be seen in the centre above the door.

West Moor Pit, Killingworth.

George returned to Killingworth Colliery, again as a brakesman. Meanwhile, his sister, Eleanor, known as Nelly, came to live with him at the West Moor cottage and looked after little Robert.

The brakesman's reputation as a man who was good at fixing machinery was growing and he became friends with Nicholas Wood, a young, educated trainee manager at the colliery (managers were known as "viewers"). Wood saw in Stephenson a man of great potential and the two friends must have encouraged each other in their enthusiasm for the budding art of engineering. In later years, Robert Stephenson was to be apprenticed to Wood, who rose to become head viewer.

In 1812 George's talents were recognised when he was appointed enginewright by the Killingworth Colliery owners, the Grand Allies. The "allies" were four powerful businessmen headed by Thomas Liddell, who later became Lord Ravensworth.

This was a major step forward for George. His pay was increased to £100 a year and he was now officially regarded as a highly skilled worker with overall responsibility for operation, maintenance and repair of the colliery's machinery. He was also called upon to build stationary engines for haulage work underground. This saved costs by cutting down on the number of pit ponies needed.

Besides tending the machinery at Killingworth, George carried out engineering and mechanical duties at the Grand Allies' other mines and his income was further increased by jobs he did for collieries they did not own.

But this self-made man of energy had received virtually no formal education. His achievements were therefore all the more remarkable and clearly show his enormous talent for engineering.

Although Stephenson regarded himself as the equal of any educated man, he nevertheless rated education highly. He saw it as the way to progress in the world. With education, a mechanic or engineer would gain increased recognition from men of wealth, men who increasingly relied upon engineering skills to help their businesses.

George was therefore determined that his son Robert would have the education he had lacked. The relatively prosperous enginewright now had a great deal more money and was able to send his son first to an elementary school at Longbenton, near Killingworth, and then to an educational

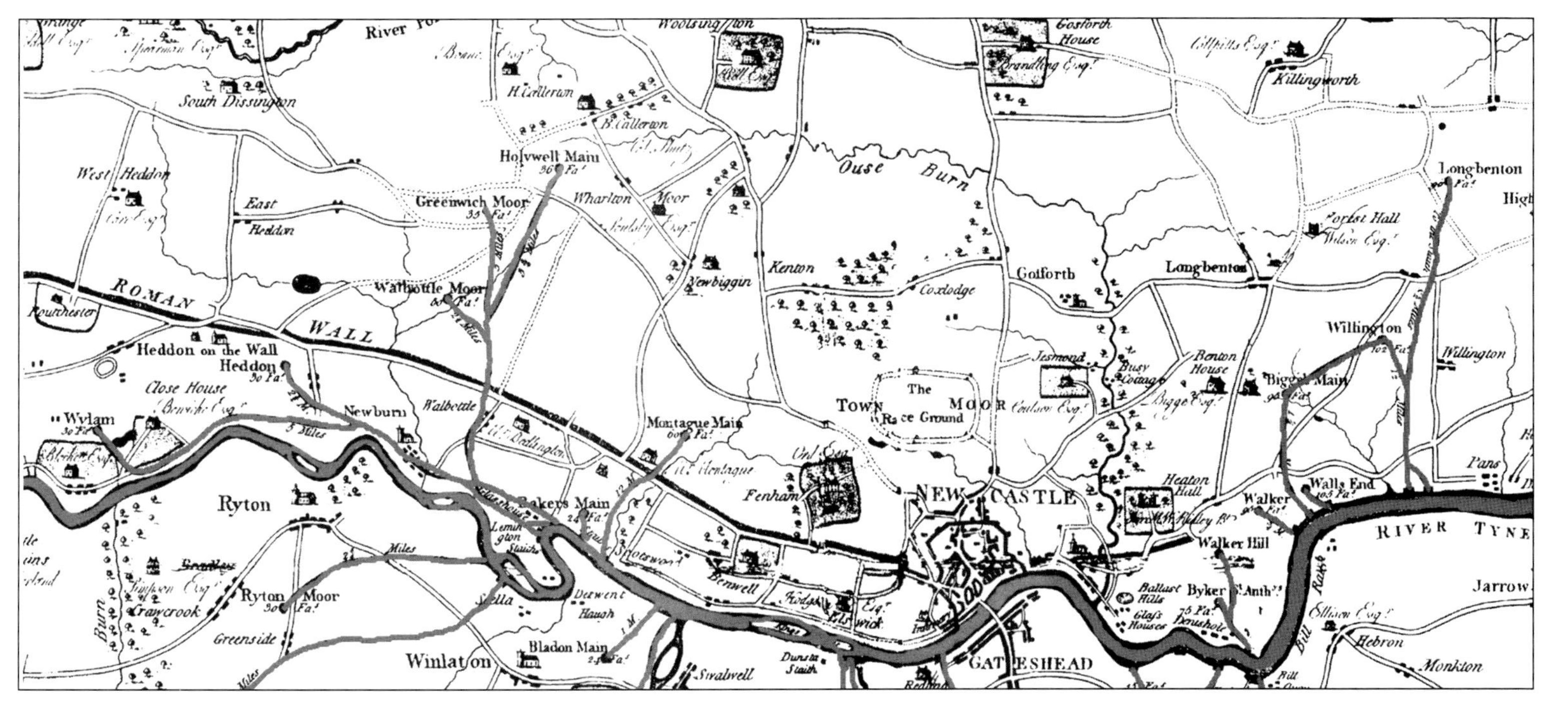

Gibson's coalfield map of 1787 shows the Tyneside area where George and Robert Stephenson spent their formative years. Wylam is to the far left, Killingworth is top right. Below, the sundial built by George and Robert in 1816.

establishment known as Dr Bruce's Academy, in Percy Street, Newcastle. Robert studied there from the age of 11 and rubbed shoulders with children from comfortably-off families. Later, George's son joined Newcastle's Literary and Philosophical Society and this further advanced his education.

As Robert learned, so George learned. The father began hearing of scientific and other subjects from his son and was eager to acquire knowledge of them. They studied together, helping each other, in the cottage at West Moor.

Among the fruits of this period was a sundial which they built together and placed above the main door of their home. Today the property is appropriately known as Dial Cottage and the sundial is still above the door, a poignant reminder of the closeness of father and son.

Andy Guy

Locomotive Fever

The invention and development of the steam locomotive was to a great extent stimulated by the Napoleonic Wars. Armies needed horses and these wars led to a shortage of horses and to fodder becoming very expensive. Mine owners were therefore willing to experiment with alternative forms of haulage for their loaded waggons. However, George Stephenson was by no means the first man to devise a "travelling engine". The steam locomotive was invented by Cornishman Richard Trevithick, the son of a tin mine manager. Starting with models, Trevithick built his first full-size locomotive in 1801 and tried it out on roads in Cornwall. But it was not a railway engine.

A more significant development came in 1804 when he constructed a locomotive for a railed waggonway at Pen-y-Daren in South Wales. It did not run for long because it was too heavy for the iron rails.

News of this locomotive reached the owner of Wylam Colliery, Christopher Blackett, and he was impressed. Such an engine might possibly be of use in combating the problem of horses and fodder. He therefore commissioned Richard Trevithick to design a locomotive for the colliery.

The inventor is reported to have visited Tyneside and the engine, with flanged wheels, was constructed to his designs at John Whinfield's iron and brass foundry in Pipewellgate, Gateshead, in 1804-1805. John Steele, a North-East born colleague of Trevithick, is believed to have contributed greatly to the project. But like the Pen-y-Daren engine this locomotive was excessively heavy and is believed to have damaged its wooden rails during trials at the foundry. Blackett was probably put off by this drawback. The locomotive was never used by the colliery and was instead employed as a stationary engine at the foundry. Even so, it is possible that George Stephenson heard of this engine from friends or even witnessed some of the test runs.

However, other men took up Trevithick's ideas and developed them. Indeed, the Tyneside area became the major test-

The engine that Richard Trevithick designed for Wylam Colliery. It was built at John Whinfield's Gateshead foundry in 1804-1805.

ing and development ground for the "travelling engine". Cornwall was undoubtedly the birthplace of the locomotive, but the North-East was the cradle in which it was nurtured and honed into workable form, driven by the need to transport coal as cheaply as possible to the staiths.

George Stephenson was one of those men who designed locomotives for use in the North-East in the wake of Trevithick's invention, but, contrary to the popular impression, he was not the first to do so.

The year 1812 saw Tyneside-born colliery viewer John Blenkinsop and engineer Matthew Murray complete a "rack" locomotive for a mine railway in the Leeds area. Murray was probably its designer with Blenkinsop patenting the rack-rail system. The driving wheel featured cogs which slotted into a rack rail as the engine moved along, but it was slow and lop-sided.

William Hedley's Puffing Billy, *which worked at Wylam from c.1813 until 1862. It was used to haul coal to the staiths at Lemington.*

This awkwardness of motion did not, however, prevent his ideas from being tested in the North-East. At least two Blenkinsop-Murray locomotives were tried out for a short time on Tyneside's Kenton and Coxlodge waggonways in c.1813, not far from Killingworth. George is likely to have seen these engines and to have learned from them.

Also in c.1813 William Hedley, the viewer at Wylam Colliery, backed by the mine's owner, Christopher Blackett, entered the engine stakes. He developed a locomotive which did not use cogged wheels like the Blenkinsop-Murray model. This smooth-wheeled engine ran on the Wylam Waggonway, which had been relaid with iron rails. Hedley was among those who found that smooth wheels could run on smooth rails without the need for cogs or a rack. The principle of "adhesion" to the track had now been established.

Hedley and those men who assisted him, Timothy Hackworth and John Forster, almost certainly learned from the Blenkinsop-Murray engines.

The Wylam viewer's first engine suffered from defects, but he went on to direct the building of three others. It may be that Timothy Hackworth was their principal designer. These heavy "puffers" steamed past the cottage where George had been born, an early portent of the railway revolution that was to come.

We know that one of these famous engines was called *Wylam Dilly* and another *Puffing Billy*. They are still in existence. *Puffing Billy* can be seen in the Science Museum, London, and *Wylam Dilly* in the Royal Museum of Scotland, Edinburgh.

It seems that Hedley's locomotives were relatively efficient, particularly when fitted with eight instead of four wheels, and they undoubtedly led useful working lives pulling the loaded coal waggons to Lemington Staiths.

Puffing Billy had a long career, working for the colliery for nearly 50 years. Built in c.1813, it was used until 1862.

Two other North-East men also entered the field around about this time. In c.1812-13 William Chapman, a highly talented engineer, designed and had built a locomotive which operated by means of chain haulage. It was supplied to Heaton Colliery, Newcastle, and tested for over a year. John Buddle, viewer and partner at the colliery, fully backed the construction of this engine, even paying for a patent to be taken out for it in 1812. He was also responsible for the locomotive's trials and is likely to have given technical advice on the project.

The Heaton engine was not William Chapman's only venture in building iron horses. A second engine designed by him was constructed for use at Lambton Colliery in County Durham, where Buddle was also a viewer. It was built by engineering workshop owner Phineas Crowther in Newcastle.

In addition, research has revealed that a locomotive was tried out on wooden rails at Wallsend Colliery, where Buddle held the same post. This "travelling engine", also designed by Chapman, was known as the *Steam Elephant*, and was later transferred to a colliery at Washington. However, it was eventually returned to Wallsend Colliery where it was used on iron rails. The engine ran by adhesion to the track. A working replica of the *Steam Elephant* can now been seen at the Beamish Museum, County Durham.

Tyne & Wear Archives

The Steam Elephant, *designed by William Chapman. It was used at Wallsend Colliery.*

George Stephenson almost certainly learned from all or some of these pioneers. Modern research suggests that Chapman and Buddle may have helped George with his earliest concepts and that he was also influenced by the Blenkinsop-Murray engines.

It could be argued that the spur of seeing the Blenkinsop-Murray, Hedley and Chapman locomotives steam along the rails provided Stephenson with the motivation to produce a better one of his own, although we cannot be certain that he saw them all in action. It is more likely, however, that his employers, the Grand Allies, did not want other mine owners to gain an advantage over them by using a cheaper form of transport than horses. They would have been happy for George to experiment with a "travelling engine".

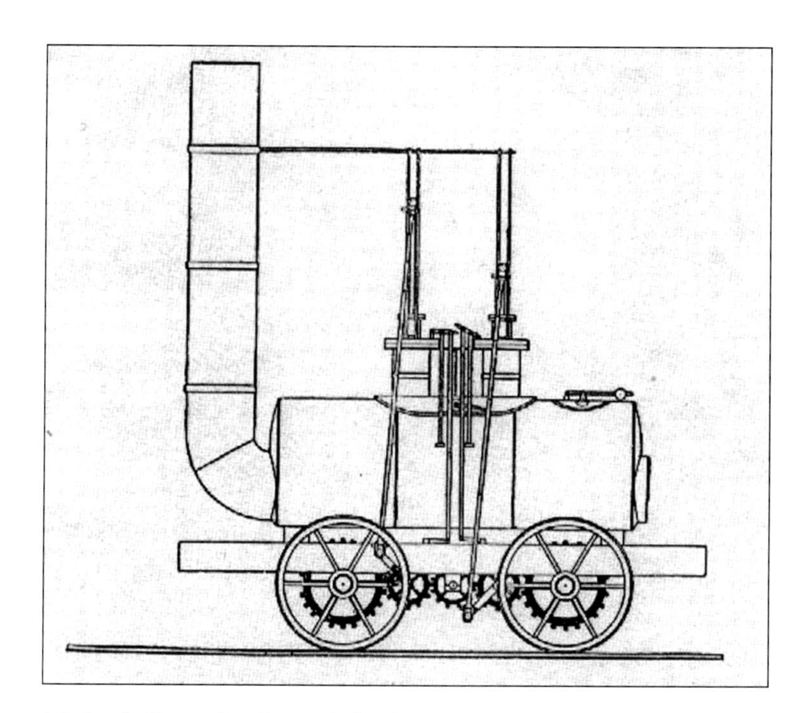

My Lord, *George Stephenson's first locomotive, constructed in 1814.*

In 1814 he therefore constructed his first locomotive at the Killingworth Colliery workshops which he named *My Lord* (come accounts say it was called *Blucher*) and which ran on iron rails and had flanged wheels. It was a step which would lead him to fame and fortune. On July 25 of that year the engine was successfully put into operation on the Killingworth Waggonway, which ran close to Dial Cottage. *My Lord* achieved four or possibly five miles per hour as it pulled a train of waggons.

The use of iron for rails was an important advance. Wooden ones were too weak to withstand the great weight of locomotives. However, the first metal rails were of cast iron and George Stephenson found even these lacked the degree of strength needed. He therefore turned his attention to developing improved rails.

George consulted William Losh, who was a partner in Losh, Wilson & Bell's Walker Ironworks, Newcastle, and together they developed better cast iron rails which were installed on the Killingworth Waggonway.

In 1819 George began directing the laying of a new railway for Hetton Colliery in County Durham. Part of this line, which ran to staiths near the mouth of the River Wear at Sunderland, was operated by three locomotives designed by Stephenson, with self-acting inclines and stationary engines being used to move the waggons along other sections. It was

Bedlington Iron Works in 1827, where wrought iron rails were perfected.

opened in 1822.

The Hetton Colliery line became something of a showpiece for George's railway building and locomotive design talents.

A further step forward occurred in 1821 when John Birkinshaw, an engineer at Michael Longridge's Bedlington Ironworks in Northumberland, perfected wrought iron rails. George realised these were superior to the cast iron type he had produced with Losh. Wrought (malleable) iron was stronger and could be made into much longer lengths, thus reducing the number of joints needed.

Dial Cottage, Killingworth, photographed in 1895. West Moor Pit can be seen beyond.

Meanwhile, he had been building more locomotives at Killingworth and he continued to improve and refine them, working at ways of increasing power and ensuring greater smoothness of running.

My Lord was followed by two engines of greater efficiency and power. In all, the highly talented enginewright produced 16 locomotives at Killingworth. These fruitful years laid the foundation of his success in launching the epoch of steam railways. George was gripped by locomotive fever, becoming an ardent champion of the engine which moved along rails. It was George's designs which proved to be the most practical and efficient at a time when interest in steam railways was growing.

But as we have seen, behind him stood a host of other pioneers whose contribution had been of equal, if not greater importance, men such as Blenkinsop, Murray, Chapman, Buddle, Steele, Hedley, Forster and Hackworth. All had played a part in developing Trevithick's initial spark of ingenuity.

The Geordie Lamp

Mining has always been a dangerous occupation. However, in the early 19th Century it was many times more hazardous than it is today. Among the greatest perils facing the men as they worked underground were gases of various kinds which had the potential to cause fatal explosions if they came into contact with the naked flame of a candle or oil lamp.

Commonplace in mine workings, these gases, including hydrogen, made the possibility of an explosion an everyday risk for the pitmen, who might die of burns or suffocation by fumes after the blast. A wall of flame could sweep through the tunnels and sometimes the explosion would bring tons of rock crashing down, trapping the men. Their unprotected lights were the problem and to many people it must have seemed there was no solution.

Killingworth Colliery, along with other mines in the North-East, suffered its share of such tragedies, the danger being posed by hydrogen issuing from fissures in the rock. For example, more than 20 men were killed as the result of gas explosions at the colliery in 1806 and 1809. George Stephenson had personal experience of these tragedies and it is not surprising that he should have brought his mind to bear on the problem.

It was in August 1815 that George began carrying out experiments to devise a "safety lamp" protected from the

High Pit, Killingworth Colliery. Hydrogen gas was a great danger to the miners at this and other pits.

A naked flame, in common use before the advent of the safety lamp, was a terrible hazard.

gases. Some of these experiments took place down one of the Killingworth Colliery pits and involved carrying lighted candles near "blowers". It was, of course, extremely dangerous.

His eventual idea was to surround an oil flame with a protective glass cylinder and to encase this in a tin cylinder. Three versions of the lamp were produced, each one an improvement on the other. In the first version, air was allowed to reach the flame by means of a tube at the base of the lamp. In the third version, air was admitted to the tin cylinder and to the top and base of the glass cylinder by numerous small holes.

Meanwhile, in London the nationally famous scientist Sir Humphrey Davy was also working on the problem and he too drew up plans for a safety lamp, which by coincidence were identical in principle, though not in form, to Stephenson's. The truth is that both men had developed the same idea independently of one another. However, George, quite unintentionally, pipped Davy to the post by having his lamp in use before Davy's.

Davy announced his plan for a lamp at a meeting of the Royal Society in London in November 1815. The following month, Stephenson demonstrated his lamp, which became known as the Geordie Lamp after its inventor, at a meeting of Newcastle's Literary and Philosophical Society. But, unlike Davy's, the Stephenson lamp was already in use at Killingworth Colliery. He had taken it into the mine in late October 1815 after having it made by a Newcastle tinsmith. The glass tube was supplied by the Northumberland Glass House.

Two years later George was to write: "This lamp was tried in Killingworth Colliery on 21st October, 1815. The idea I had long entertained and the drawing was shown to several persons employed in that concern, two months before the day above mentioned, when I carried it with safety into a part of the mine where a strong blower of hydrogen was coming off. An experiment which was immediately repeated in the presence of two persons employed in that concern."

The two men who accompanied Stephenson into the mine on this momentous occasion were his friend Nicholas Wood and another fellow worker, under-viewer John Moodie.

George was clearly a man of great courage. The hydrogen could be heard hissing out from a crack in the rock. Indeed, it was coming out more strongly than usual. When Wood

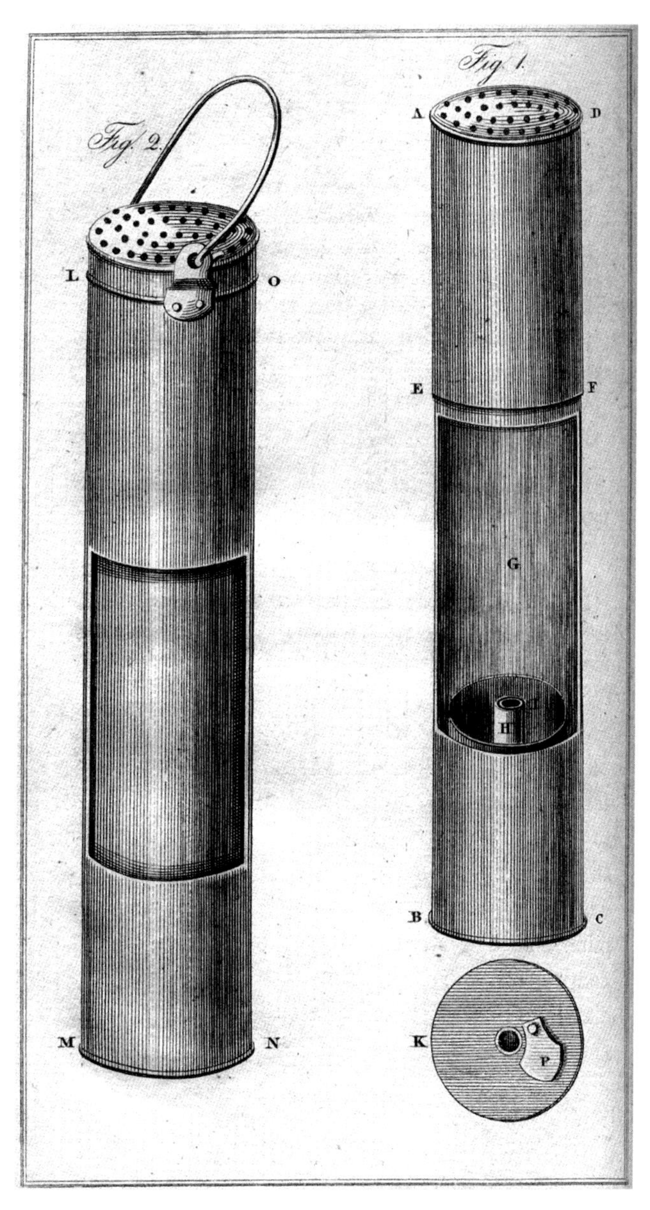

"This lamp was tried in Killingworth Colliery, on the 21st of October 1815 ... when I carried it with safety into a part of the mine where a strong blower of hydrogen was coming off."

and Moodie heard this powerful "blower" they decided to go no further, but Stephenson pressed onwards. However, before he reached the spot where the gas was issuing from the mine roof the flame went out. But there was no blast.

He then returned to his companions, re-lit the flame and moved towards the "blower" for a second time. On reaching it, he held the lamp directly in front of the escaping hydrogen. Again, there was no explosion. Instead, the flame went out, as before.

George returned once more to Wood and Moodie and he persuaded them to approach closer to the "blower". He then repeated the experiment. For a third time, there was no blast. This emboldened Wood who is believed to have held the lamp in front of the "blower" himself. All lived to tell the tale. The bravery of Stephenson had been extraordinary.

By the time George gave his lecture in December 1815, the third, improved version of his safety lamp had been used in the mine.

However, a furious dispute erupted when Sir Humphrey Davy was hailed nationally as the inventor of the safety lamp and awarded £2,000. It was even alleged that George had in some way borrowed Davy's ideas. Stephenson's supporters in the North-East were stung by these claims, asserting that their man had been the real inventor.

North-East men of wealth and power, including the Grand Allies, Charles Brandling and William Losh, were stout in their defence of Stephenson. In 1817 a North-East committee of inquiry was set up, which met at the Assembly Rooms, Newcastle, to look into the issue. Witnesses testified to the committee that George's lamp was the first in use and his name was cleared of the allegation that he had borrowed

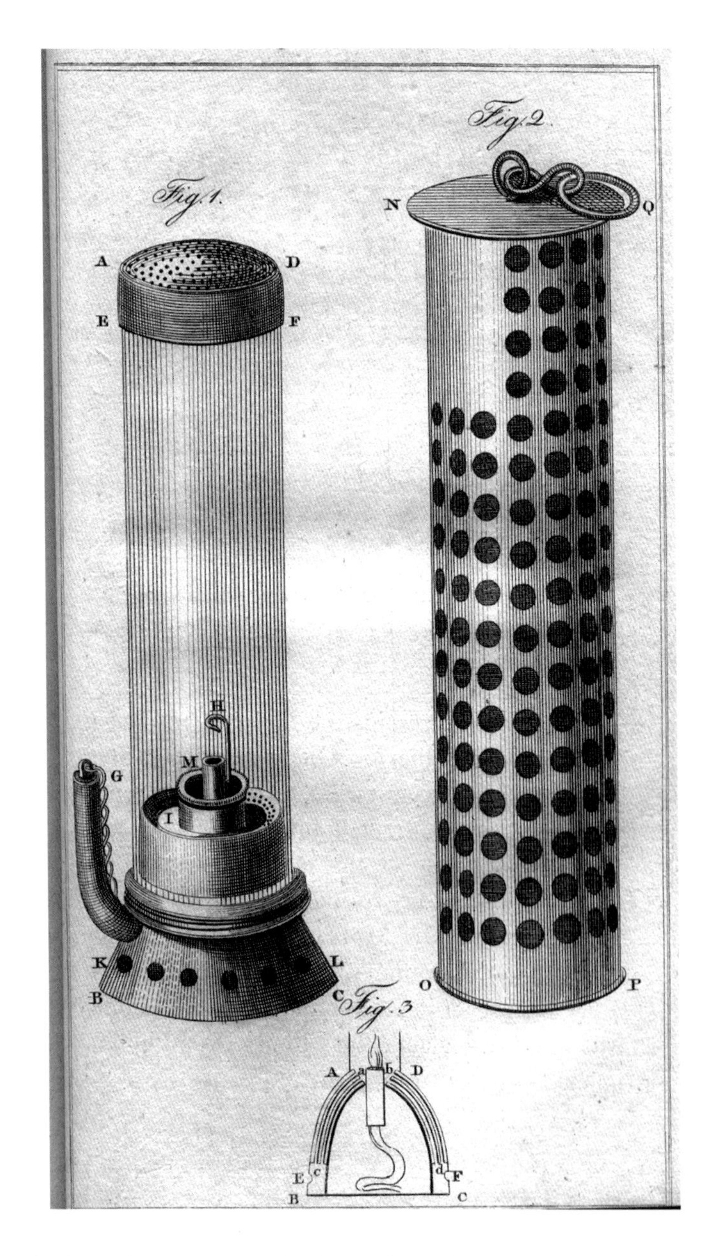

The lamp that was eventually adopted by Killingworth Colliery.

Davy's ideas.

The committee "ascertained that as early as August 1815" Stephenson "was busied with various experiments upon the air proceeding from blowers in coal mines". The enginewright was accordingly awarded £1,000 and a silver tankard by his supporters.

Stephenson had discovered that hydrogen would not explode because of the small holes in the cylinders. He wrote: "My habits, as a practical mechanic, make me afraid of publishing theories, and I am by no means satisfied that my own reasons, or any of those I have seen published, why hydrogen gas will not explode through small apertures, are the true ones. It is sufficient for our present purpose that the fact has been discovered, and that it has been successfully applied in the construction of a lamp that may be carried with perfect safety into the most explosive atmosphere."

The committee of inquiry acknowledged Stephenson's invention with a resolution: "Mr George Stephenson discovered the fact that explosion of hydrogen gas will not pass through tubes and apertures of small dimensions, that he was the first to apply that principle in the construction of a safety lamp, and that he was therefore, entitled to a public reward."

In a letter to the *Philosophical Magazine* of March 1817, George "solemnly" asserted that he had designed a lamp "with small perforations, without knowing that Sir Humphrey had adopted the same idea, and without receiving any hints of his experiments..."

The Geordie Lamp was favoured by miners in many pits throughout the North-East. The Davy version, which was surrounded by a wire gauze, was less popular in the region. It did not have a glass cylinder.

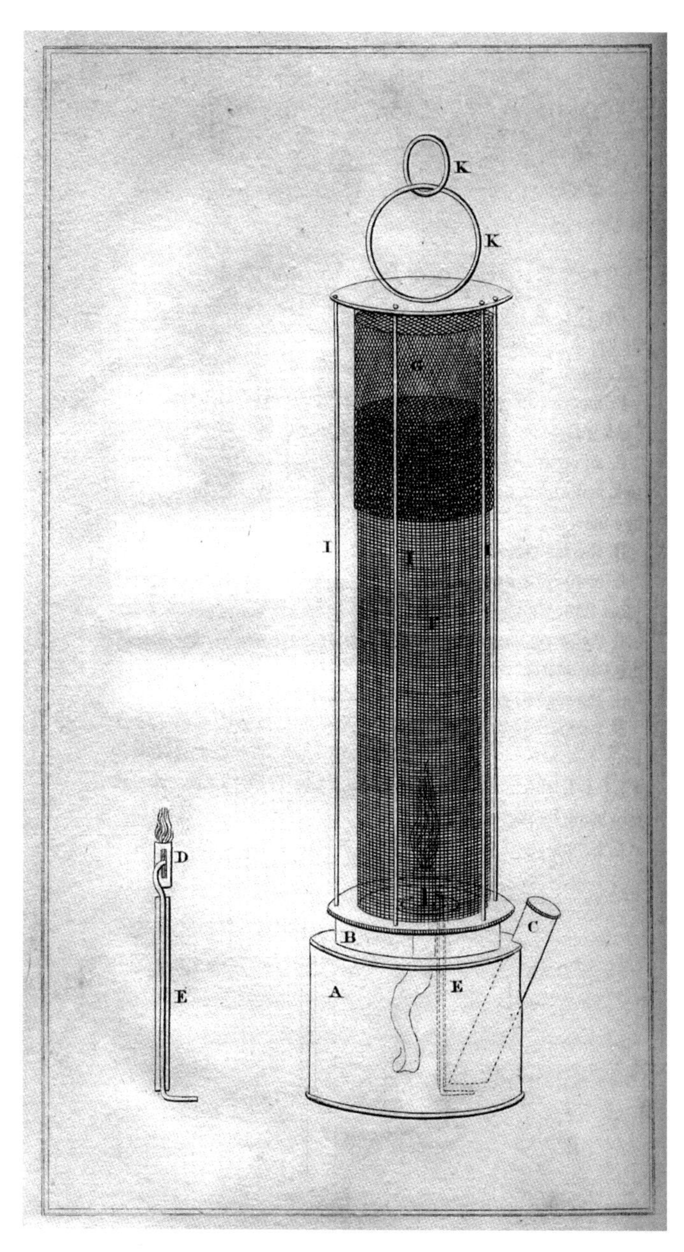

The Davy Lamp. Its rival, the Geordie Lamp, was more popular in the North-East.

Occasionally, a draught might cause the flame from a Davy to pass through the gauze and make contact with explosive gas. The Geordie, with its protective glass cylinder, did not suffer from this defect, the glass enclosing the flame. In addition, the upper part of the Davy was said to have a tendency to become overheated, another hazard in gaseous conditions. The Geordie's glass cylinder was again an asset because it helped to prevent this happening. However, in c.1820 Stephenson re-designed his lamp, surrounding it with a gauze, similar to Davy's. But he retained the vital glass cylinder.

It is possible that the term "Geordie", the name by which people born on Tyneside are affectionately known to this day, originates from the lamp's use by the Tyneside miners. What is certain, however, is that the invention saved countless men from death, giving off a reassuring light as the North-East miners toiled amid the black depths. The Geordie Lamp proved to be their trusted friend.

A Quaker Railway

On September 27 1825 the Stockton and Darlington Railway in County Durham was opened amid tumultuous celebrations. George Stephenson planned and directed the building of this pioneering line, the first public railway in the world to use steam locomotives.

The line was constructed mainly to carry coal from the pits of the Shildon district of County Durham to a quayside on the River Tees at Stockton. It featured a branch track running to Darlington and included passing loops.

The project had been largely the brainchild of Edward Pease, an enterprising Quaker wool merchant of Darlington, and other businessmen, many of them also Quakers.

Initially it was envisaged that horses would be the main motive power on the railway, with possibly some stationary engines. But Pease met George Stephenson and was eventually persuaded, after a visit to Killingworth, that steam locomotives should be used on part of the line.

Stephenson was a passionate advocate of steam power and Pease was impressed by his enthusiasm. George's successful work on the Hetton Colliery Railway may also have been a factor in swaying the decision in his favour.

Stephenson recommended wrought iron rails for the new route and that they should be supplied by the Bedlington Ironworks. This was a surprising move, since George had an interest in promoting his own cast iron rails which he had patented with William Losh.

However, he chose to set aside potential monetary gain and recognise the superiority of wrought iron.

Edward Pease further backed Stephenson when he contributed money for the setting up of the world's first locomotive factory, at South Street, off Forth Street, Newcastle, in 1823. The factory became known as the Forth Street Works and it was here that the locomotives for the Stockton and Darlington Railway were built.

The business formed to run the works was to be known as Robert Stephenson and Company, and consisted of a part-

The opening of the Stockton and Darlington Railway, 1825

Locomotion *pulling the train at the opening of the Stockton and Darlington Railway in 1825.* Locomotion *today is on display at Darlington Railway Museum.*

nership between George and his son Robert, Edward Pease and Michael Longridge, owner of the Bedlington Ironworks.

The name of the company revealed the faith which George Stephenson had in his son's abilities. Robert became the managing partner in charge of running the works at the age of 20.

The first two engines for the railway produced at Forth Street were *Locomotion* and *Hope*. These were followed by *Diligence* and *Black Diamond*.

For the opening of the line in 1825 George and his brother James were at the controls of *Locomotion*, which was linked to a passenger coach called the *Experiment* and

The Experiment, *a passenger coach, which was used at the opening.*

22 coal waggons in which seats had been installed for other travellers. These were joined by 10 loaded coal wagons which had traversed part of the line by means of stationary engines, inclines and horses.

Locomotion then set off for Stockton from Shildon Lane Ends, the train crowded with people, many of them standing or holding on to the sides as all seats had been taken. These excited passengers cheered wildly and when the line ran alongside a road, people in horse-drawn carriages followed the train. All were amazed by the spectacle of Stephenson's extraordinary, fiery iron horse. When the train reached Stockton Quay it was greeted by thousands of cheering people who had come to see this new wonder of the world. Despite stoppages due to the derailment of a waggon and a technical problem with the engine, the train had reached its destination without mishap or injury to anyone. Cannons, church bells and bands saluted the train's arrival at the quay as well as the vast crowd. A banquet was then held at Stockton Town Hall to celebrate the triumph of the steam locomotive, with George Stephenson the undisputed hero of the day. Yet the whole project would never have become a reality without the backing of the Quaker businessmen, and in particular the open-minded Edward Pease.

Edward Pease, the Quaker businessman who backed the construction of the Stockton and Darlington Railway.

Andy Guy

Replicas of Locomotion, *left, and the* Steam Elephant *at Beamish North of England Open Air Museum, Co. Durham.*

Rocket to Success

Robert Stephenson had helped his father carry out the survey work for the Stockton and Darlington Railway and was in charge of the Forth Street Works for a year. But events were to take an unexpected turn. In 1824 Robert left England and went to South America for three years as engineer to silver and gold mines in Colombia. The project was not a success. In the meantime, the works did not fare well either.

When he returned to England in late 1827 his father was directing the building of the Liverpool and Manchester

Left, George, and right, his son Robert. Their engine, Rocket, *built at the Forth Street Works, Newcastle, was chosen for the Liverpool and Manchester Railway, which opened in 1830.*

Railway which was to become the world's first public line, carrying passengers as well as freight, operated entirely by steam locomotives.

After battling against fierce opposition from canal owners, the railway company eventually obtained parliamentary permission to begin work on the link between the two great northern cities. George was appointed engineer in charge of its construction.

The self-taught man from Tyneside rose to the immense challenge before him. The task involved the building of more than 60 bridges and the laying of a line across the treacherous peat bog known as Chat Moss. Encountering numerous difficulties, George had drains dug either side of the route across the bog, then vast amounts of ballast tipped into this quagmire, together with heather, moss and timber.

Very slowly, but surely, a firm foundation in the shape of a raised bank was created to carry the line. Those who predicted it would be impossible to put a railway across Chat Moss had been proved wrong.

The nine-arched Sankey Viaduct on the Liverpool and Manchester Railway. Each arch has a 50-foot span.

Engineering prowess: the Mount Olive Cutting, nearly two miles long, on the Liverpool and Manchester Railway.

Stephenson's other major feats of civil engineering along the 30-mile route included the building of the Edgehill Tunnel which led into and out of Liverpool and the nine-arched Sankey Viaduct.

However, the Liverpool and Manchester Railway Company took some time to decide whether to use stationary engines or locomotives on the line. Eventually the scales began to tip in favour of locomotives and trials were arranged on a part of the line at Rainhill, near Liverpool, to find out which type of engine might be best suited to pull the trains.

The locomotives which entered for these tests had to meet

The Forth Street works, the world's first purpose-built locomotive factory. The works were actually in South Street, just off Forth Street.

strict requirements. For example, each engine could weigh no more than six tons and had to travel up and down the track for a total distance of 60 miles. The prize for winning the trials was £500. The real prize, however, was adoption of the winning type of engine by the railway – if its directors could be persuaded to abandon the idea of rope haulage using stationary engines.

Meanwhile, at the Forth Street Works in Newcastle Robert Stephenson was again at the helm. Now, his main task was to produce an engine which would win the Rainhill Trials.

George, who was living in Liverpool, communicated by letter with his son and together they planned a locomotive which was to prove a stunning success. They were greatly helped by Henry Booth, treasurer of the Liverpool and Manchester Railway, who suggested the idea for an improved boiler.

The engine which took shape at Forth Street was to be called the *Rocket* and its triumph was due in no small measure to the multi-tube boiler proposed by Booth. The 25 tubes, made of copper, ran along the whole length of the boiler, thus greatly increasing efficiency and power.

It seems that Robert attended to every detail with meticulous care and George made suggestions by letter. All three men therefore made a contribution to the creation of the new iron horse upon which all hopes were pinned.

The *Rocket* also featured a "blast pipe". George had first used this device in his early locomotive days at Killingworth. This involved channelling the exhaust steam into the chimney, thus creating a draught for the fire and increasing power.

The *Rocket*, complete with its revolutionary boiler, was first tried out by Robert on the Killingworth Waggonway, by this time referred to as a railway. On this test run it achieved a top speed of 12mph, pulling a tender, five waggons and carrying 40 men. Tyneside was thus the scene of this famous metal steed's debut. Today, the *Rocket* is displayed at London's Science Museum.

After the test run, the locomotive was taken back to Forth Street and when all was ready the *Rocket* was dismantled, lowered into horse-drawn waggons and taken by road from Newcastle to Carlisle. From there it was transported by canal to Bowness on Solway and then loaded on to a steamship which sailed to Liverpool.

The Rainhill Trials were held in October 1829. Besides,

the *Rocket*, the competing engines included the *Sans Pareil*, which had been built by Timothy Hackworth, a highly talented engineer who had spent his early life at Wylam and had helped William Hedley with the construction of his engines. He had become, on the recommendation of George Stephenson, the engineer in charge of the Shildon workshops of the Stockton and Darlington Railway.

During Robert's spell in South America and George's absence while he was building the Liverpool line, Timothy Hackworth had made improvements to the engines on the Stockton and Darlington route following two fatal accidents when engines blew up. He designed a fine locomotive, the *Royal George*, which proved highly successful on the line. It was the first six-coupled engine.

Now, at Rainhill, Hackworth was a competitor, his Shildon-built *Sans Pareil* vying against the *Rocket* for the £500 prize and ultimate adoption by the new railway.

However, it was the *Rocket* which proved superior to all its rivals. Watched by a large crowd who cheered as if they were at a race meeting, each locomotive began to go through its paces. One by one, over several days, the other competitors suffered problems and the *Rocket* emerged triumphant, proving itself to be the most reliable engine. It was also fast, achieving almost 30mph. Later, following the trials, George took the engine on a run without waggons, during which it is said to have notched up 35mph.

The result was that the stationary engines idea was dropped and Newcastle-made locomotives of the *Rocket*-type were chosen. The Forth Street Works now became a hive of activity as the engines took shape under the careful eye of Robert Stephenson. The brilliant son was playing the leading

Rocket, *the engine which won the Rainhill Trials. It was built at the Forth Street Works under the direction of Robert Stephenson.*

role in taking the development of the locomotive to a more advanced stage.

The main part of the early works was situated on the east side of South Street, a turning off Forth Street. The premises were extended in 1825 when an iron foundry was added. After c.1830 the works expanded on the western side of South Street. Besides locomotives, the company also produced parts for railway waggons and many stationary engines for various industrial uses.

The Liverpool and Manchester Railway opened on September 15 1830 with a procession of eight trains which

A Victorian illustration of 1892 depicting the opening of the Liverpool and Manchester Railway, September 15 1830.

started out from Liverpool. This parade of steam was led by a locomotive named *Northumbrian,* appropriately driven by George. The other engines included *Phoenix*, driven by Robert, and *Rocket*, with assistant engineer Joseph Locke at the controls.

Northumbrian pulled a train of rich, famous and aristocratic guests and ran along one track of the two-track line. The seven remaining trains occupied the other track.

Among the top guests in the *Northumbrian's* carriages were the Duke of Wellington, Cabinet minister William Huskisson, actress Fanny Kemble and Earl Grey, who was responsible for the landmark electoral reform Bill of 1832 and whose memorial column is still one of Newcastle's most impressive landmarks.

All went well at first, with George's train, on its own line, slowing down and stopping on occasions so that the guests could get a good view of the various bridges and other features. At Parkside, the train halted for water and it was planned that at this point the other trains would steam past to allow the celebrity guests to gain a view of them.

However, the occasion was marred by tragedy when William Huskisson, who had alighted from his carriage and was standing in the gap between the two tracks, was hit by the *Rocket*. The somewhat frail minister had stumbled over and his legs had fallen across the track reserved for the passing trains.

George swiftly decided to take Huskisson for treatment to the nearest station, which was Eccles, near Manchester. The unfortunate politician, who received first aid at the scene of the accident, was lifted into a carriage, the rest of the carriages were detached from the train, and *Northumbrian*, still with Stephenson at the controls, steamed away to Eccles. However, Huskisson died from his injuries several hours later.

The trains on the opening day did eventually steam into Manchester where vast crowds had gathered and they also managed to return to Liverpool without further mishap.

But despite the untimely death of Huskisson, the accident did not affect the ultimate success of the line and the onward march of steam railways which the two Stephensons had begun. Soon the father and son were involved in the construction of other railways across Britain. Locomotive "fever" was followed by railway-building "mania".

The Bridge Builder

Robert Stephenson had married a London girl, Frances Sanderson, also known as Fanny, not long after his return from South America and they set up home together in Greenfield Place, Newcastle, just off the city's Westgate Road. *Rocket*, and a more advanced engine, *Planet*, were built while he was living there. Later, the couple moved to London.

Meanwhile, the Stephensons continued to progress in the burgeoning world of railways. Father and son were appointed technical advisers for the creation of Belgium's railway network and the Forth Street Works supplied locomotives to that country. In the 1830s the works also turned out some of the earliest engines for lines in Russia, the United States, Germany and Austria-Hungary.

In Britain, the Stephensons were kept busy as engineers to numerous other lines. George was chief engineer to the London & Northern, London & South Wales, North Midland, North Midland & York, Whitby & Pickering and Manchester & Leeds lines. Robert's work included the Canterbury and Whitstable, the London & Birmingham, the Leicester & Swannington (together with his father), and the Chester & Holyhead lines.

However, railways needed bridges and it was as a bridge builder that Robert was to earn lasting fame.

The superb two-deck High Level Bridge across the River

An 1860's photograph of Robert Stephenson's High Level Bridge. Robert left to posterity a series of impressive bridges. The two-deck High Level is 1,337 feet long and supported by massive sandstone pillars.

The opening of the High Level Bridge by Queen Victoria in 1849.

Tyne between Gateshead and Newcastle was designed by this brilliant man. It brought the railway from the south into Newcastle for the first time. Hitherto the line had terminated at Gateshead.

The lower deck carries a road and footpaths, the upper deck the railway. Work began on driving the first pile into the river bed in April 1846. Robert Stephenson was present to witness Naysmith's newly-invented steam hammer start this work.

The 1,337ft-long bridge was officially opened by Queen Victoria in 1849. London and Newcastle were now linked by the rails of iron which were beginning to cover every corner of Britain. Victoria crossed the bridge on her way from Scotland to the South of England.

Although the royal opening of the High Level Bridge had taken place on September 28 1849, a passenger train had crossed a temporary wooden bridge on the foundations of the new structure for the first time over a year earlier, on August 29 1848, while the massive permanent bridge, supported on huge pillars, was still undergoing construction.

Railway developer George Hudson, known as the "Railway King", led a party of dignitaries, including the mayors of Newcastle and Gateshead, on to a train drawn up at Gateshead Station.

One of the carriages contained a party of ladies and another the band of Messrs. Hawks and Crawshay, of Gateshead, the firm responsible for the ironwork of the permanent bridge. When the train, pulled by a powerful engine, entered the temporary bridge it was greeted with a salute from cannons positioned on the Newcastle side.

The *Illustrated London News* declared that "the train smoothly and quietly, at a moderately quick pace, and without the slightest interruption or accident, glided from Durham to Northumberland". It "afforded passengers a view of the ancient town of Newcastle at once novel and extensive".

The bells of Newcastle's St Nicholas Church rang out and the thousands of people who had gathered on each side of the Tyne cheered enthusiastically. The train crossed without mishap and arrived safely at Manors Station, then part of the North Shields Railway. Afterwards, the guests, who numbered over 70, were entertained to lunch by the Mayor of Newcastle at the Queen's Head. Not surprisingly, toasts were drunk to both George and Robert Stephenson.

The last arch of the permanent bridge was finished on June 7 1849. The completion of the work was marked by a party of councillors and aldermen from Gateshead who met the workmen on the lower deck to celebrate. According to the *Gateshead Observer*, they drank sherry and "strong ale".

Two years later the *Gateshead Observer* commented: "An unfounded fear had often been expressed that horses would be alarmed by the noise overhead, when a train was passing

The Royal Border Bridge spanning the River Tweed at Berwick, photographed c.1890. Also designed by Robert, it was opened by Queen Victoria in 1850. The imposing viaduct features 28 arches. A railway at last stretched without interruption all the way from London to Edinburgh.

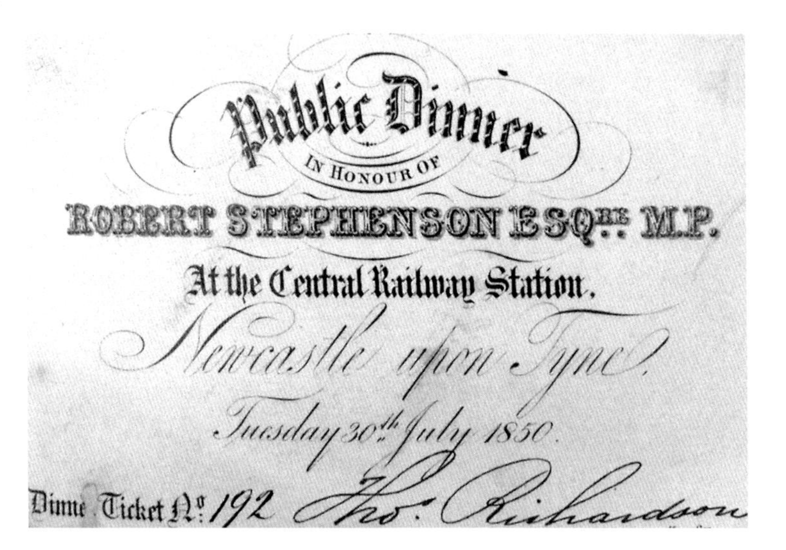

In July 1850 a public dinner was held just inside the main entrance of Newcastle Central Station to honour the achievements of Robert Stephenson. Exhibited were paintings of the High Level Bridge, the Menai Bridge and the Royal Border Bridge. In his speech, reported in the Illustrated London News, *Robert remembered: "It was but as yesterday that he was engaged as an assistant in tracing the line of the Stockton and Darlington Railway … He marvelled at all that had been accomplished."*

along the upper deck. Sir John Fife assured the Newcastle Council that he had made the experiment with some of the most irritable horses that existed, and found this fear to be chimerical."

In late August 1850 the Royal Border Bridge across the River Tweed at Berwick, also designed by Robert, was opened by Queen Victoria, this time on her way northwards to Scotland. The imposing viaduct features 28 arches. A railway at last stretched without interruption all the way from London to Edinburgh.

In the same year, Robert's impressive Britannia Tubular Bridge across the Menai Straits between the mainland of North Wales and Anglesey was opened. He also designed the magnificent tubular Victoria Bridge over the St Lawrence River at Montreal, opened in 1859, which connects Canada with the United States, two bridges in Egypt, and one across the River Conway in North Wales.

Robert's hard work on the *Rocket* and his achievements in railway building had been eclipsed by his renown as a bridge builder. Today, the great structures of the High Level and Royal Border bridges, spanning equally great rivers, still stand as testaments to his brilliance.

Newcastle's Forth Street Works continued to build engines throughout the rest of the 19th Century. However, by 1900 orders for locomotives were now so numerous and many of the engines were so large that the factory was becoming too small. This led to the company building a new works at Darlington in 1901-02. Most of the old works at

Forth Street was sold to the neighbouring company of Hawthorn Leslie at Forth Banks.

The history of Hawthorn Leslie can be traced back to 1817 when Robert Hawthorn set up a business as a millwright in Forth Banks. Robert, who was joined by his brother William, later began building locomotives and marine engines as well as undertaking general engineering work. In 1872 R&W Hawthorn, as the firm was known, opened a marine engine building works at St Peter's in the East End of Newcastle.

The St Peter's Works supplied many of the engines for ships built by Andrew Leslie's yard at Hebburn on the south side of the Tyne. The two firms merged in 1885 to become Hawthorn Leslie & Company. After the First World War, this company built some of the earliest diesel locomotives in a joint venture with English Electric.

The Robert Stephenson & Hawthorns works c.1950, viewed from the nearby railway in Newcastle.

However, the name of Stephenson eventually returned to Newcastle. In 1937 the locomotive department of Hawthorn Leslie merged with Stephenson's to become Robert Stephenson & Hawthorns Ltd. While the Darlington works concentrated mainly on larger locomotives, Newcastle's Forth Banks manufactured small ones, gaining a good reputation for industrial railway engines.

But although the 1937 merger was a major development, there had been a much earlier association between the names of Stephenson and Hawthorn. Robert and William Hawthorn's father, Robert, who had been engineer at Water Row Pit, was the man who had recommended George Stephenson for the job of brakesman in charge of the engine at Willington Quay Ballast Hill in 1803. Robert senior had installed the engine. The world of the Tyneside mechanics was a small but enduring one.

Andy Guy

Father and Son

What kind of men were George and Robert Stephenson? We know that George was a confident, assertive man with a strong faith in his own ideas. Some might call him aggressively self-confident at times. He was not the sort to back down in an argument. His assertiveness and ambitious nature undoubtedly helped him to battle his way from obscurity to fame and fortune. He was, of course, assisted by his great technical abilities, by men who backed him such as Quaker Edward Pease and by a generous measure of good luck. He was a man who found himself positioned in the right place at the right time and he grasped the opportunity.

George Stephenson from a sketch by Edward Whymper.

But despite his ambitious nature, George was capable of kindness and generosity to his friends and relatives. He was also, as we have seen, a man of courage. This is illustrated by the tests he carried out in the mine for his safety lamp.

Robert comes across to us as a quieter, more thoughtful character, both polite and cultured. He was well liked by most of those who knew him, being charitable and patient in nature. Like his father, he possessed a technical genius but unlike George had the benefit of a full education.

Both father and son refused the offer of knighthoods. George was not keen on titles. He seems to have respected the ordinary working man more than those with wealth and power, although he was not averse to mixing with the aristocracy on occasions.

It was in 1820 that George married again, 15 years after the death of his beloved Fanny. This time, his bride was Elizabeth Hindmarsh, who by all accounts was an "old flame" from his days as a brakesman at Black Callerton Colliery. Newburn Church was again the scene of his wedding and they lived at Dial Cottage until 1822.

In later years George, by this time a wealthy man, set up residence at Tapton House, a mansion in Chesterfield, Derbyshire. He was the part-owner of coal mines, an iron-works and limestone quarries in the area. Thus the man who started life as the son of a colliery worker joined the ranks of the rich and famous. In our own times, his portrait has featured on the back of the £5 sterling note.

George and Elizabeth, who was known as Betty, had no children. After 25 years of marriage, Betty died in 1845 and her husband was once again a widower. But the railway pioneer was to marry again. His third bride was Ellen Gregory, who had been his housekeeper at Tapton. They were wed in February 1848.

However, the marriage was to be short-lived. George Stephenson died six months later, on August 12 1848, at the age of 67. He had contracted pleurisy. The man destined to be called the father of steam railways was buried at Holy Trinity Church, Chesterfield, beside his second wife.

Robert and his wife Fanny lived comfortably together in London, enjoying the lifestyle of rich Victorians. Despite their wealth, they had no children, which was a source of great sadness to them. Fanny died of cancer in 1842. It was a formidable blow to Robert and he never remarried.

In 1847 the great bridge builder was elected MP for Whitby and he became president of the Institution of Civil Engineers in 1855. He now had success and fame but personal happiness eluded him in the last years of his life.

On October 12 1859 Robert died at his London home at the age of 55. His funeral on October 21 at Westminster Abbey, where he was buried, was attended by many wealthy and famous mourners. It was a far cry from the humble cottage at Willington Quay where he had been born.

Robert Stephenson, the successful engineer. He and his wife, Fanny, had no children, which was a source of great sadness to them.

In Newcastle, Shields and Sunderland the shops, banks

and offices were closed for the afternoon of the funeral and ships in the river flew their flags at half-mast as a mark of respect for this feted son from the river's banks.

The bells of Newcastle's St Nicholas Church rang a muffled peal at intervals throughout the day. Appropriately, the church was the scene of a special service in memory of Robert. About 1,200 men from the Forth Street Works, together with men from Messrs. Hawks, Crawshay & Company, attended the service to pay their last respects to the man who had presided over the creation of powerful engines and mighty bridges.

But the father and son did not need any formal monument. Their monument already existed in the shape of locomotives and railways. For the Stephensons had left to posterity a legacy of inestimable value to civilisation which had revolutionised passenger and goods transport. The invention developed with such enthusiasm and perseverance on the banks of the Tyne was to spread with an unstoppable momentum throughout the globe.

George and Robert Stephenson's Rocket *was remembered when this fascinating replica engine was on show at the Newcastle 900 celebrations, July 1980, at Newcastle Civic Centre.*

Chronology

1781 George Stephenson born on June 9 in cottage at Wylam, Northumberland.

1801 George obtains job as brakesman at Dolly Pit, Black Callerton Colliery.

1802 George Stephenson and Fanny Henderson married at Newburn Church in November.

1803 The newlyweds move to cottage at Willington Quay, where George has obtained job as brakesman at the ballast hill. The couple's son, Robert, born there on October 16.

1804 George obtains job as brakesman at Killingworth Colliery and family move to cottage (later known as Dial Cottage) at West Moor.

1805 Couple's daughter, also called Fanny, born. She dies after only three weeks.

1806 George's wife, Fanny, dies of consumption, aged 37.

1812 George promoted to enginewright at Killingworth Colliery.

1814 George constructs his first locomotive, *My Lord*. It is tried out on the Killingworth Waggonway on July 25.

c.1814-15 Robert Stephenson begins attending Dr Bruce's Academy in Percy Street, Newcastle, at the age of 11 after early schooling in Longbenton.

1815 George tests his safety lamp at Killingworth Colliery on October 21. Third version of the lamp is in use at colliery by late November. He gives a demonstration of the lamp to a meeting of Newcastle's Literary and Philosophical Society in December.

1816 George and Robert construct a sundial for their cottage at West Moor.

1819-22 George engineers the building of the Hetton Colliery Railway, County Durham. His locomotives are used on part of the line.

1820 George and Elizabeth Hindmarsh married at Newburn Church.

1823 George and Robert Stephenson, together with partners Edward Pease and Michael Longridge, set up the Forth Street locomotive works in Newcastle. It is the first locomotive factory in the world. The first engines for the Stockton and Darlington Railway are built there.

1825 The Stockton and Darlington Railway, engineered by George, is opened on September 27 with the train being pulled by *Locomotion*. It is the first public railway in the world to use steam locomotives.

1829 Robert and Frances Sanderson married in June in London. They move to a home at Greenfield Place, Newcastle, close to the city's Westgate Road.

1829 Rocket, built at the Forth Street works in Newcastle, wins the Rainhill Trials in October.

1830 The Liverpool and Manchester Railway, engineered by George, opens on September 15. The first public railway in the world carrying passengers as well as freight to be operated entirely by steam locomotives. George leads the parade of trains with the locomotive *Northumbrian*. Cabinet minister William Huskisson dies after being struck by *Rocket*.

1842 Robert's wife, Frances, known as Fanny, dies.

1845 George's second wife, Elizabeth, known as Betty, dies.

1848 George marries Ellen Gregory in February.

1848 George Stephenson dies, aged 67, at Tapton House, Chesterfield, Derbyshire, on August 12. He is buried in Holy Trinity Church, Chesterfield.

1849 High Level Bridge across Tyne between Gateshead and Newcastle officially opened by Queen Victoria on September 28. Bridge designed by Robert. It brings the railway from the south into Newcastle for the first time.

1850 Royal Border Bridge across Tweed at Berwick officially opened by Queen Victoria on August 29. Bridge designed by Robert.

1859 Robert Stephenson dies on October 12, aged 55, in London. He is buried in Westminster Abbey.

The Victoria Bridge over the St Lawrence River, Montreal. It opened a few months after Robert Stephenson's death and was at one time the largest bridge in the world.

Some sources consulted

A Description of the Safety Lamp Invented by George Stephenson and now in use at Killingworth Colliery (1817)

Report upon the claims of Mr George Stephenson Relative to the Invention of his Safety Lamp (Newcastle, 1817)

North Eastern Locomotive Pioneers 1805 to 1827: A Reassessment, Andy Guy, Researcher, Beamish, the North of England Open Air Museum

Steam and Speed: Railways of Tyne and Wear from the Earliest Days, Andy Guy (Tyne Bridge Publishing, 2003)

The Life of George Stephenson, Samuel Smiles (Fourth Edition, revised with additions, John Murray, 1857)

George and Robert Stephenson, L.T.C. Rolt (Longmans, 1960)

George Stephenson, Hunter Davies (Weidenfeld & Nicolson, 1975)

Where Railways Were Born, Philip R.B. Brooks (Wylam Parish Council, 1979)

North of England News and Advertiser, 1859

Gateshead Observer, 1849

Illustrated London News